This journal belongs to:

_____

_____

Introduction

The epidemic of anxiety is more prevalent in this generation than in all the generations before us.

With the constant bombardment from the outside world hitting us from every direction almost every hour of the day, It's no wonder that so many people struggle to have control over their own minds and thoughts. We are basically running on autopilot almost involuntarily. It's second nature to pick up your phone and be scrolling through something before you even realize what you are doing.

The practice of mindfulness, however, is intentional. It brings us back to the present moment and forces us to pay attention. Why is this important for anxiety sufferers? When you purposefully pay attention, you become more aware of your thoughts, emotions, and triggers. Becoming aware of the root of our pain is the first step in being able to release it. Practicing mindful writing with a combination of gratitude cultivation each day can have profound effects on your mental health. It will not only assist you with anxiety relief but also help guide you to restore your sense of well-being, peace, and calm.

Rest assured you are in the right place.

May this Journal be an ally in your *healing journey* through anxiousness.

How to use this journal

Mindful writing prompts - This section is to help guide you in a small writing exercise daily that will help you provoke thoughts in a mindful and personal way.

What am I thankful for today? - Take the time to list all of the things that you are grateful for each day. The practice of gratitude can transform our way of thinking and help us cultivate a positive mindset.

A calming thought for today - This space is intended for writing a simple affirming or calming thought that you may carry with you and repeat back in the times when you need it most.

Self-care check-in - Take the time to check in the boxes of the personal needs you have met for the day and then write down how you may improve your daily self-care habits or what you may do the next day.
Making time for yourself and meeting your own needs is vital for maintaining a balanced, peaceful, and calm you.

Meditation moment - Intended to help you get in the habit of meditation practice. Whether that be through, guided meditations, calming meditation music, repeating mantras, or simply breathing. Take a moment to check in and lean into a small practice and record how you feel afterward.

Inspiring quotes - You may notice that there are quotes throughout the journal to help with your self reflection and inspire you throughout your journaling time.

Set it Free - (Free-writing) section is meant to be a zone in which you can feel free to express anything you want to. Free writing has proven effects to help you release self-judgment or judgment from others and in turn, helps you increase your self confidence. Writing is also one of the most effective ways to release trapped emotions inside us.

DATE:_____   S M T W T F S

Think of a place that is very meaningful to you. What kind
of emotions do you experience when you are in this place?

What am I thankful for?

_____
_____
_____
_____
_____
_____

A calming thought

_____
_____
_____

Meditation Moment: _____ minutes

○ Guided   ○ Silent   ○ Background Noise / Music _____

○ Mantra _____   ○ No mantra

○ Other _____

Self-Care Check-In:

○ Did I get enough sleep _____

○ Did I nourish my body with food _____

○ Did I hydrate my body with water _____

What did I do to make myself feel happy today?

_____
_____
_____
_____
_____

"FEW OF US EVER LIVE IN THE *present*. WE ARE FOREVER ANTICIPATING WHAT IS TO COME OR REMEMBERING WHAT HAS GONE."

LOUIS L'AMOUR

SET IT FREE

Write down some things that you wish people would say
to you when you are feeling overwhelmed or frustrated?

What am I thankful for?

_____

_____

_____

_____

_____

_____

A calming thought

_____

_____

_____

Meditation Moment: _____ minutes

◯ Guided   ◯ Silent   ◯ Background Noise / Music _____

◯ Mantra _____   ◯ No mantra

◯ Other

Self-Care Check-In:

◯ Did I get enough sleep _____

◯ Did I nourish my body with food _____

◯ Did I hydrate my body with water _____

What did I do to make myself feel happy today?

_____

_____

_____

_____

_____

"YOU CAN'T *stop* THE WAVES, BUT YOU CAN *learn* TO SURF."

JON KABAT-ZINN

SET IT FREE

Picture yourself in your perfect state of mind. What kind of things are you doing and saying?

⟨⟨⟨⟨⟨⟨

What am I thankful for?

_____
_____
_____
_____
_____
_____
_____
_____
_____

A calming thought

_____
_____
_____

Meditation Moment: _____ minutes

○ Guided   ○ Silent   ○ Background Noise / Music _____

○ Mantra _____   ○ No mantra

○ Other _____

Self-Care Check-In:

○ Did I get enough sleep _____

○ Did I nourish my body with food _____

○ Did I hydrate my body with water _____

What did I do to make myself feel happy today?

_____
_____
_____
_____
_____

"OUR LIFE IS SHAPED BY OUR *mind*, FOR WE BECOME WHAT WE *think*"

BUDDHA

SET IT FREE

Think of a song that you really, really love to listen to. What type of song or genre is it? What feelings does it invoke? Does it make you happy, calm, pumped, angry, or sad? Simply observe and then write your thoughts below.

What am I thankful for?

_____

_____

_____

_____

_____

_____

A calming thought

_____

_____

_____

Meditation Moment: _____ minutes

○ Guided   ○ Silent   ○ Background Noise / Music _____

○ Mantra _____   ○ No mantra

○ Other _____

Self-Care Check-In:

○ Did I get enough sleep _____

○ Did I nourish my body with food _____

○ Did I hydrate my body with water _____

What did I do to make myself feel happy today?

_____

_____

_____

_____

_____

"YOU DON'T HAVE TO CONTROL YOUR *thoughts*. YOU JUST HAVE TO STOP LETTING THEM CONTROL YOU."

DAN MILLMAN

SET IT FREE

Look around you, pick something rather ordinary and
describe it as you were seeing it for the first time.

What am I thankful for?

_____

_____

_____

_____

_____

_____

_____

_____

A calming thought

_____

_____

_____

Meditation Moment: _____ minutes

○ Guided   ○ Silent   ○ Background Noise / Music _____

○ Mantra _____   ○ No mantra

○ Other

Self-Care Check-In:

○ Did I get enough sleep _____

○ Did I nourish my body with food _____

○ Did I hydrate my body with water _____

What did I do to make myself feel happy today?

_____

_____

_____

_____

_____

_____

"OUR ANXIETY DOES NOT COME FROM *thinking* ABOUT THE FUTURE, BUT FROM WANTING TO *control* IT."

KAHLIL GIBRAN

SET IT FREE

S M T W T F S

When was the last time you felt truly loved?
Describe how that felt to you.

〰〰〰〰〰

_____

_____

_____

_____

_____

_____

_____

_____

_____

_____

_____

_____

_____

_____

_____

_____

_____

_____

_____

_____

_____

_____

_____

_____

_____

What am I thankful for?

_____

_____

_____

_____

_____

_____

_____

_____

A calming thought

_____

_____

_____

Meditation Moment: _____ minutes

◯ Guided   ◯ Silent   ◯ Background Noise / Music _____

◯ Mantra _____   ◯ No mantra

◯ Other _____

Self-Care Check-In:

◯ Did I get enough sleep _____

◯ Did I nourish my body with food _____

◯ Did I hydrate my body with water _____

What did I do to make myself feel happy today?

_____

_____

_____

_____

_____

"WHEN I LET GO OF
WHAT I AM, I
become WHAT I
WANT TO BE."

LAO TZU

SET IT FREE

What is something that is weighing on your mind right now?

What am I thankful for?

_____
_____
_____
_____
_____
_____

A calming thought

_____
_____
_____

Meditation Moment: _____ minutes

○ Guided   ○ Silent   ○ Background Noise / Music _____

○ Mantra _____   ○ No mantra

○ Other _____

Self-Care Check-In:

○ Did I get enough sleep _____

○ Did I nourish my body with food _____

○ Did I hydrate my body with water _____

What did I do to make myself feel happy today?

_____
_____
_____
_____
_____

"I MAY NOT BE WHERE
I WANT TO BE, BUT I'M
thankful FOR NOT
BEING WHERE I USED
TO BE."

HABEEB AKANDE

SET IT FREE

DATE:_____   S M T W T F S

Stop what you are doing and breathe in 3 long and slow
breaths... Now, how was your day today?

_____

_____

_____

_____

_____

_____

_____

_____

_____

_____

_____

_____

_____

_____

_____

_____

_____

_____

_____

_____

_____

_____

_____

_____

What am I thankful for?

_____
_____
_____
_____
_____
_____
_____

A calming thought

_____
_____
_____

Meditation Moment: _____ minutes

◯ Guided   ◯ Silent   ◯ Background Noise / Music _____

◯ Mantra _____   ◯ No mantra

◯ Other _____

Self-Care Check-In:

◯ Did I get enough sleep _____

◯ Did I nourish my body with food _____

◯ Did I hydrate my body with water _____

What did I do to make myself feel happy today?

_____
_____
_____
_____
_____

"DO NOT LET THE
BEHAVIOR OF OTHERS
DESTROY YOUR
inner peace ."

DALAI LAMA

SET IT FREE

Think of a person in your life whom you may not have kind feelings toward. Take some time to write about how you might display compassion to this person and how that might feel for you.

What am I thankful for?

_____

_____

_____

_____

_____

_____

_____

_____

A calming thought

_____

_____

_____

Meditation Moment: _____ minutes

○ Guided   ○ Silent   ○ Background Noise / Music _____

○ Mantra _____   ○ No mantra

○ Other _____

Self-Care Check-In:

○ Did I get enough sleep _____

○ Did I nourish my body with food _____

○ Did I hydrate my body with water _____

What did I do to make myself feel happy today?

_____

_____

_____

_____

_____

_____

"WHEN THINGS *change* INSIDE YOU, THINGS *change* AROUND YOU."

UNKNOWN

SET IT FREE

DATE:_____   S M T W T F S

What is something you can start doing today that will help
you break out of your comfort zone?

What am I thankful for?

_____

_____

_____

_____

_____

_____

A calming thought

_____

_____

Meditation Moment: _____ minutes

○ Guided   ○ Silent   ○ Background Noise / Music _____

○ Mantra _____   ○ No mantra

○ Other _____

Self-Care Check-In:

○ Did I get enough sleep _____

○ Did I nourish my body with food _____

○ Did I hydrate my body with water _____

What did I do to make myself feel happy today?

_____

_____

_____

_____

_____

"THE *battles* THAT COUNT AREN'T THE ONES FOR GOLD MEDALS. THE STRUGGLES WITHIN YOURSELF—THE INVISIBLE BATTLES INSIDE ALL OF US—THAT'S WHERE IT'S AT."

JESSE OWENS

SET IT FREE

Whatever season you may be in, (Winter, Spring, Summer, Fall) What are 5 things you are grateful for in that season?

What am I thankful for?

_____

_____

_____

_____

_____

_____

_____

_____

A calming thought

_____

_____

_____

Meditation Moment: _____ minutes

○ Guided   ○ Silent   ○ Background Noise / Music _____

○ Mantra _____   ○ No mantra

○ Other _____

Self-Care Check-In:

○ Did I get enough sleep _____

○ Did I nourish my body with food _____

○ Did I hydrate my body with water _____

What did I do to make myself feel happy today?

_____

_____

_____

_____

_____

"IF YOU LOOK AT WHAT YOU *have* IN LIFE, YOU'LL ALWAYS HAVE MORE. IF YOU LOOK AT WHAT YOU DON'T HAVE IN LIFE, YOU'LL *never* HAVE ENOUGH."

OPRAH WINFREY

SET IT FREE

Write down some of the things that are heavy and weighing you down at the moment. Then, close your eyes and picture each thought you wrote as a rock that you are holding in your hand. Picture yourself throwing the rock as far as you can into an ocean or a river. Repeat it for all the things you wrote down. How did this process feel to you?

What am I thankful for?

_____
_____
_____
_____
_____
_____

A calming thought

_____
_____
_____

Meditation Moment: _____ minutes

◯ Guided   ◯ Silent   ◯ Background Noise / Music _____

◯ Mantra _____   ◯ No mantra

◯ Other _____

Self-Care Check-In:

◯ Did I get enough sleep _____

◯ Did I nourish my body with food _____

◯ Did I hydrate my body with water _____

What did I do to make myself feel happy today?

_____
_____
_____
_____
_____

"IT DOES NOT
MATTER HOW
slowly YOU GO AS
LONG AS YOU DO
NOT STOP."

CONFUCIUS

SET IT FREE

DATE:_____ S M T W T F S

What is a color that makes you feel happy? Think about
what things are typically associated with that color. Record
what you observe. What may that have to do with you?

What am I thankful for?

_____

_____

_____

_____

_____

_____

_____

A calming thought

_____

_____

_____

Meditation Moment: _____ minutes

◯ Guided   ◯ Silent   ◯ Background Noise / Music _____

◯ Mantra _____   ◯ No mantra

◯ Other _____

Self-Care Check-In:

◯ Did I get enough sleep _____

◯ Did I nourish my body with food _____

◯ Did I hydrate my body with water _____

What did I do to make myself feel happy today?

_____

_____

_____

_____

_____

_____

"A WALK IN *nature*, WALKS THE SOUL BACK HOME."

MARY DAVIS

SET IT FREE

DATE:_____ 　　S M T W T F S

What are some things in your life that you have observed change?

What am I thankful for?

_____

_____

_____

_____

_____

_____

_____

_____

A calming thought

_____

_____

_____

Meditation Moment: _____ minutes

○ Guided   ○ Silent   ○ Background Noise / Music _____

○ Mantra _____   ○ No mantra

○ Other _____

Self-Care Check-In:

○ Did I get enough sleep _____

○ Did I nourish my body with food _____

○ Did I hydrate my body with water _____

What did I do to make myself feel happy today?

_____

_____

_____

_____

_____

Anxiety DOES NOT EMPTY TOMORROW OF ITS SORROWS, BUT ONLY EMPTIES TODAY OF ITS STRENGTH."

CHARLES SPURGEON

SET IT FREE

DATE:_____   S M T W T F S

What are some things that I can control in my surroundings?
What are some things I have no control over?

〰〰〰〰〰

What am I thankful for?

_____
_____
_____
_____
_____
_____
_____

A calming thought

_____
_____
_____

Meditation Moment: _____ minutes

○ Guided   ○ Silent   ○ Background Noise / Music _____

○ Mantra _____   ○ No mantra

○ Other _____

Self-Care Check-In:

○ Did I get enough sleep _____

○ Did I nourish my body with food _____

○ Did I hydrate my body with water _____

What did I do to make myself feel happy today?

_____
_____
_____
_____
_____

"NOT EVERYTHING THAT *weighs* YOU DOWN IS YOURS TO CARRY."

ANONYMOUS

SET IT FREE

Take a second to think of an animal, preferably the first animal that pops into your head. Now, think of the characteristics of that animal. What kind of personality does it have? Color, size, tendencies, and climate it prefers. Do you have any similarities to this animal?

What am I thankful for?

_____

_____

_____

_____

_____

_____

A calming thought

_____

_____

_____

Meditation Moment: _____ minutes

○ Guided   ○ Silent   ○ Background Noise / Music _____

○ Mantra _____   ○ No mantra

○ Other _____

Self-Care Check-In:

○ Did I get enough sleep _____

○ Did I nourish my body with food _____

○ Did I hydrate my body with water _____

What did I do to make myself feel happy today?

_____

_____

_____

_____

_____

"FEELINGS COME AND GO LIKE CLOUDS IN A WINDY SKY. *Conscious* BREATHING IS MY ANCHOR."

THICH NHAT HANH

SET IT FREE

What are 3 things that drain your energy? What are 3
things that make you feel energized?

What am I thankful for?

_____

_____

_____

_____

_____

_____

_____

A calming thought

_____

_____

Meditation Moment: _____ minutes

○ Guided   ○ Silent   ○ Background Noise / Music _____

○ Mantra _____   ○ No mantra

○ Other _____

Self-Care Check-In:

○ Did I get enough sleep _____

○ Did I nourish my body with food _____

○ Did I hydrate my body with water _____

What did I do to make myself feel happy today?

_____

_____

_____

_____

_____

"ALMOST EVERYTHING WILL WORK AGAIN IF YOU *unplug* IT FOR A FEW MINUTES, INCLUDING YOU."

ANNE LAMOTT

SET IT FREE

What is something you are passionate about? Do you make time to implement that into your daily life? If not, how can you start?

What am I thankful for?

_____
_____
_____
_____
_____
_____
_____

A calming thought

_____
_____
_____

Meditation Moment: _____ minutes

◯ Guided   ◯ Silent   ◯ Background Noise / Music _____

◯ Mantra _____   ◯ No mantra

◯ Other _____

Self-Care Check-In:

◯ Did I get enough sleep _____

◯ Did I nourish my body with food _____

◯ Did I hydrate my body with water _____

What did I do to make myself feel happy today?

_____
_____
_____
_____
_____
_____

"IT'S NOT STRESS
THAT KILLS US, IT
IS OUR *reaction*
TO IT."

HANS SELYE

SET IT FREE

What does your ideal day look like? Describe in detail

What am I thankful for?

_____
_____
_____
_____
_____
_____
_____

A calming thought

_____
_____
_____

Meditation Moment: _____ minutes

○ Guided   ○ Silent   ○ Background Noise / Music _____

○ Mantra _____   ○ No mantra

○ Other _____

Self-Care Check-In:

○ Did I get enough sleep _____

○ Did I nourish my body with food _____

○ Did I hydrate my body with water _____

What did I do to make myself feel happy today?

_____
_____
_____
_____
_____

"Surrender TO WHAT IS, LET GO OF WHAT WAS, AND HAVE FAITH IN WHAT WILL BE."

SONIA RICOTTI

SET IT FREE

List 3 of your top needs. Did you have your needs met today?
What can you do to ensure that your needs get met every day?

What am I thankful for?

_____
_____
_____
_____
_____
_____
_____
_____

A calming thought

_____
_____
_____

Meditation Moment: _____ minutes

○ Guided   ○ Silent   ○ Background Noise / Music _____

○ Mantra _____   ○ No mantra

○ Other _____

Self-Care Check-In:

○ Did I get enough sleep _____

○ Did I nourish my body with food _____

○ Did I hydrate my body with water _____

What did I do to make myself feel happy today?

_____
_____
_____
_____
_____

"*Worry* IN THE
DARK CAN MAKE
IT EVEN
DARKER."

CAMRON WRIGHT

SET IT FREE

DATE: _____   S M T W T F S

What is something you can do to improve your daily
routine to manage stress and bring more ease?

What am I thankful for?

_____

_____

_____

_____

_____

_____

A calming thought

_____

_____

Meditation Moment: _____ minutes

○ Guided   ○ Silent   ○ Background Noise / Music _____

○ Mantra _____   ○ No mantra

○ Other _____

Self-Care Check-In:

○ Did I get enough sleep _____

○ Did I nourish my body with food _____

○ Did I hydrate my body with water _____

What did I do to make myself feel happy today?

_____

_____

_____

_____

_____

"ACTUALLY SPENDING TEN MINUTES CLEARING OFF ONE SHELF IS BETTER THAN *fantasizing* ABOUT SPENDING A WEEKEND CLEANING OUT THE BASEMENT."

GRETCHEN RUBIN

SET IT FREE

DATE: _____   S M T W T F S

How does your body feel right now? Are there any pain points?
What do you think may be causing those pain points?

🌿

_____

_____

_____

_____

_____

_____

_____

_____

_____

_____

_____

_____

_____

_____

_____

_____

_____

_____

_____

_____

_____

_____

What am I thankful for?

_____
_____
_____
_____
_____
_____
_____

A calming thought

_____
_____

Meditation Moment: _____ minutes

○ Guided   ○ Silent   ○ Background Noise / Music _____

○ Mantra _____   ○ No mantra

○ Other _____

Self-Care Check-In:

○ Did I get enough sleep _____

○ Did I nourish my body with food _____

○ Did I hydrate my body with water _____

What did I do to make myself feel happy today?

_____
_____
_____
_____
_____

"WORK *with* IT, NOT
AGAINST IT."

ECKHART TOLLE

SET IT FREE

What kind of person do you think other people see you as?
How does that make you feel?

What am I thankful for?

_____
_____
_____
_____
_____
_____
_____
_____

A calming thought

_____
_____
_____

Meditation Moment: _____ minutes

◯ Guided   ◯ Silent   ◯ Background Noise / Music _____

◯ Mantra _____   ◯ No mantra

◯ Other _____

Self-Care Check-In:

◯ Did I get enough sleep _____

◯ Did I nourish my body with food _____

◯ Did I hydrate my body with water _____

What did I do to make myself feel happy today?

_____
_____
_____
_____
_____

"LEAN INTO IT. THE *outcome* DOESN'T MATTER. WHAT MATTERS IS THAT YOU WERE THERE FOR IT."

CHRIS PINE

SET IT FREE

DATE:_____   S M T W T F S

Did you experience anxiety or tension today? What exactly
triggered those emotions? How did you handle it?

What am I thankful for?

_____

_____

_____

_____

_____

_____

_____

A calming thought

_____

_____

_____

Meditation Moment: _____ minutes

◯ Guided   ◯ Silent   ◯ Background Noise / Music _____

◯ Mantra _____   ◯ No mantra

◯ Other _____

Self-Care Check-In:

◯ Did I get enough sleep _____

◯ Did I nourish my body with food _____

◯ Did I hydrate my body with water _____

What did I do to make myself feel happy today?

_____

_____

_____

_____

_____

_____

"*Worrying* IS LIKE WALKING AROUND WITH AN UMBRELLA WAITING FOR THE RAIN."

UNKNOWN

SET IT FREE

DATE:_____   S M T W T F S

How can you fulfill your emotional, physical, and spiritual
self-care needs? Think of one example for each.

What am I thankful for?

_____

_____

_____

_____

_____

_____

_____

_____

A calming thought

_____

_____

_____

Meditation Moment: _____ minutes

○ Guided   ○ Silent   ○ Background Noise / Music _____

○ Mantra _____   ○ No mantra

○ Other _____

Self-Care Check-In:

○ Did I get enough sleep _____

○ Did I nourish my body with food _____

○ Did I hydrate my body with water _____

What did I do to make myself feel happy today?

_____

_____

_____

_____

_____

"STOP LETTING
PEOPLE WHO DO SO
LITTLE FOR YOU,
control SO MUCH
OF YOUR MIND,
FEELINGS, AND
EMOTIONS."

WILL SMITH

SET IT FREE

DATE: _____ S M T W T F S

What kind of energy did you release into the world today?
Describe how that made you feel, without judgment.

⋘⋘⋘

_____

_____

_____

_____

_____

_____

_____

_____

_____

_____

_____

_____

_____

_____

_____

_____

_____

_____

_____

_____

_____

_____

_____

_____

_____

What am I thankful for?

_____
_____
_____
_____
_____
_____
_____

A calming thought

_____
_____
_____

Meditation Moment: _____ minutes

○ Guided   ○ Silent   ○ Background Noise / Music _____

○ Mantra _____   ○ No mantra

○ Other _____

Self-Care Check-In:

○ Did I get enough sleep _____

○ Did I nourish my body with food _____

○ Did I hydrate my body with water _____

What did I do to make myself feel happy today?

_____
_____
_____
_____
_____
_____

"SOMETIMES YOU HAVE TO *forget* WHAT YOU FEEL AND REMEMBER WHAT YOU DESERVE"

FRIDA KHALO

SET IT FREE

Take 5 min to be outside. Pick just one thing to observe.
Describe it in as much detail as possible.

What am I thankful for?

_____

_____

_____

_____

_____

_____

A calming thought

_____

_____

_____

Meditation Moment: _____ minutes

○ Guided   ○ Silent   ○ Background Noise / Music _____

○ Mantra _____   ○ No mantra

○ Other _____

Self-Care Check-In:

○ Did I get enough sleep _____

○ Did I nourish my body with food _____

○ Did I hydrate my body with water _____

What did I do to make myself feel happy today?

_____

_____

_____

_____

_____

"BE WHO YOU ARE AND SAY WHAT YOU *feel* BECAUSE THOSE WHO MIND DON'T MATTER AND THOSE WHO MATTER DON'T MIND."

DR. SEUSS

SET IT FREE

Think of a smell that you love? What does it remind you of?
A time in the past? Childhood? How does that make you feel?

‹‹‹‹‹‹

What am I thankful for?

_____

_____

_____

_____

_____

_____

A calming thought

_____

_____

Meditation Moment: _____ minutes

○ Guided   ○ Silent   ○ Background Noise / Music _____

○ Mantra _____   ○ No mantra

○ Other _____

Self-Care Check-In:

○ Did I get enough sleep _____

○ Did I nourish my body with food _____

○ Did I hydrate my body with water _____

What did I do to make myself feel happy today?

_____

_____

_____

_____

_____

"A BEAUTIFUL
DAY BEGINS
WITH A
beautiful
MINDSET."

JOHN GEIGER

SET IT FREE

Take the time to write a thank you note to someone special in your life. Be specific and don't hold back. Consider typing it out or making a copy to give to them. You won't be sorry that you did.

What am I thankful for?

_____
_____
_____
_____
_____
_____
_____
_____

A calming thought

_____
_____
_____

Meditation Moment: _____ minutes

○ Guided   ○ Silent   ○ Background Noise / Music _____

○ Mantra _____   ○ No mantra

○ Other _____

Self-Care Check-In:

○ Did I get enough sleep _____

○ Did I nourish my body with food _____

○ Did I hydrate my body with water _____

What did I do to make myself feel happy today?

_____
_____
_____
_____
_____

"IF IT'S OUT OF YOUR HANDS, IT DESERVES *freedom* FROM YOUR MIND TOO."

IVAN NURU

SET IT FREE

What is something causing you to worry right now? If you
did absolutely nothing about it at all, what would occur?

What am I thankful for?

_____
_____
_____
_____
_____
_____
_____

A calming thought

_____
_____
_____

Meditation Moment: _____ minutes

○ Guided   ○ Silent   ○ Background Noise / Music _____

○ Mantra _____   ○ No mantra

○ Other _____

Self-Care Check-In:

○ Did I get enough sleep _____

○ Did I nourish my body with food _____

○ Did I hydrate my body with water _____

What did I do to make myself feel happy today?

_____
_____
_____
_____
_____

"AND THEN SHE
FLEW AWAY, FOR
SHE WAS FINALLY
free"

NYDIA

SET IT FREE

Made in the USA
Las Vegas, NV
27 January 2024